27 Dec 1959

For Martha Elaine

Fondly,

Florence and Bill Sabatini

THE LITTLE BRASS BAND

STORY BY

MARGARET WISE BROWN

PICTURES BY

CLEMENT HURD

HARPER & BROTHERS   NEW YORK

COCK A DOODLE DOO

EARLY IN THE MORNING,
THE LITTLE BRASS BAND CAME OVER THE HILL,
ONE BY ONE.

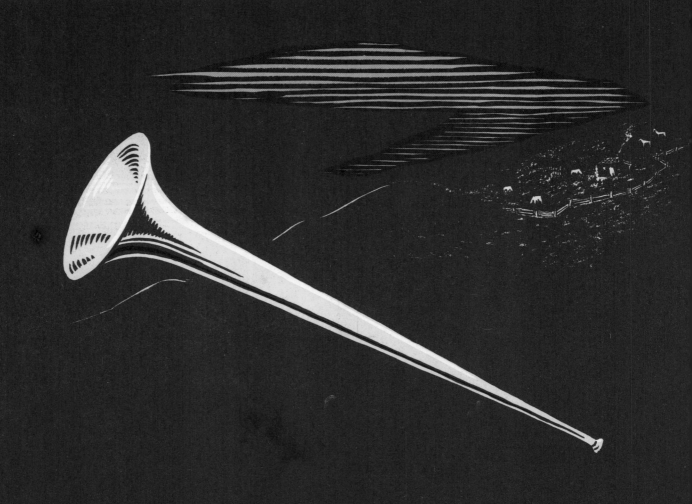

FIRST THE TRUMPET FROM A DISTANT FARM

THEN DOWN THE HILL CAME TWO GOLDEN
HORNS TO JOIN THE BAND.

A FLUTE,

A CLARINET,

AND AN OBOE

AND JUST AS THE SUN ROSE BEHIND THEM,
THE LITTLE BRASS BAND CAME OVER THE HILL.
FAR DOWN THE ROAD YOU COULD HEAR
THEM, FAR AWAY.

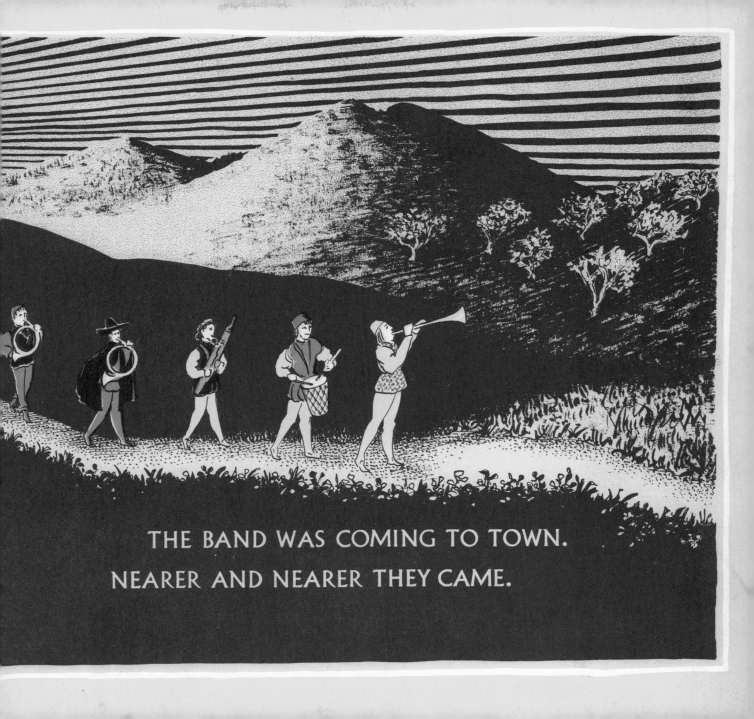

THE BAND WAS COMING TO TOWN.
NEARER AND NEARER THEY CAME.

THE OLD PEOPLE LISTENED AT THEIR WINDOWS
ON THE EDGE OF THE TOWN, AND THE CHILDREN
DANCED IN THE STREETS AS THE LITTLE BAND IN
THEIR RED COATS WITH THEIR BRASS INSTRUMENTS

ALL SHINING IN THE SUN WALKED THROUGH THE
GATE OF THE TOWN. THE MUSIC ECHOED
FROM WALL TO WALL.

AND THEN THEY MARCHED UP TO THE
LITTLEST HOUSE IN TOWN. AND THERE, BEFORE A
LITTLE WINDOW WHERE A CHILD WAS STILL ASLEEP,
THEY PLAYED A SOFT LITTLE SENTIMENTAL SONG.

AND WHEN
THEY FINISHED,
THERE WAS A
CLINK, CLINK
AS PENNIES AND OTHER COINS
SHOWERED ABOUT THEM.

THEN THE BAND MARCHED ON AND PLAYED A
LOUD AND POMPOUS TUNE UNDER THE WINDOWS
OF THE BIGGEST HOUSE IN TOWN, WHERE THE
CHIEF OF POLICE STOOD AT THE WINDOW
SHAVING HIS WHISKERS.

THEN THE LITTLE BAND WENT TO THE
TOWN SQUARE AND GAVE A BIG
CONCERT WHILE THE PEOPLE CAME AND
LAY IN THE GRASS AND LISTENED.

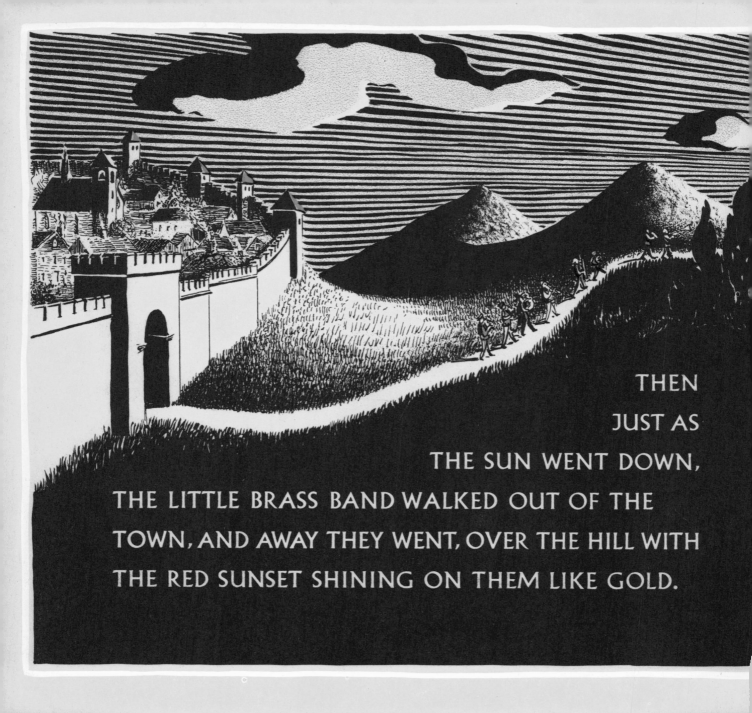

THEN
JUST AS
THE SUN WENT DOWN,
THE LITTLE BRASS BAND WALKED OUT OF THE
TOWN, AND AWAY THEY WENT, OVER THE HILL WITH
THE RED SUNSET SHINING ON THEM LIKE GOLD.

FARTHER AND FARTHER AND FARTHER AWAY
THEY WENT, UNTIL THE FLUTE, THE OBOE, AND
THE CLARINET GOT TO THE BRIDGE, AND THERE
THEY LEFT THE BAND.

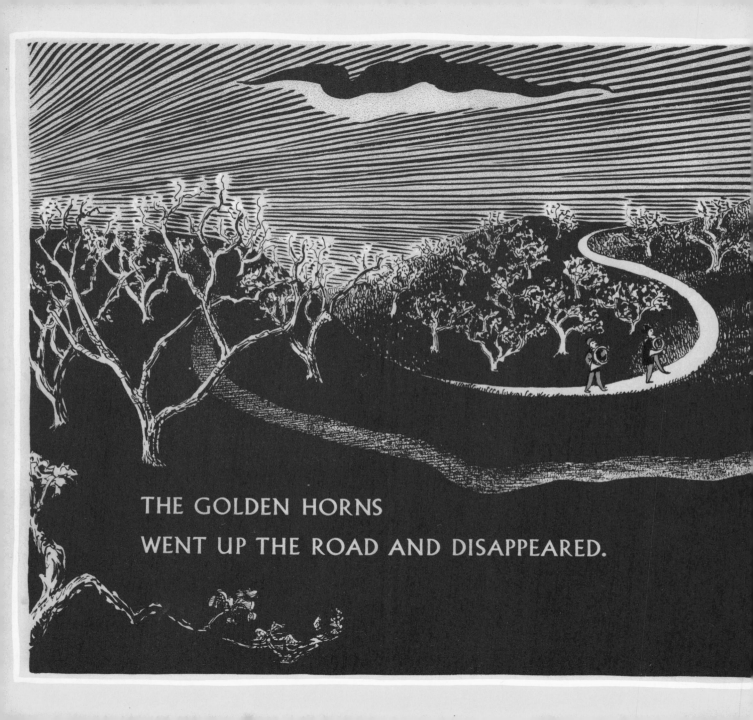

THE GOLDEN HORNS
WENT UP THE ROAD AND DISAPPEARED.

AND THE REST OF THE BAND WALKED ON
TO THE CROSSROADS, WHERE THE BASSOON
SAID GOOD-BYE.

AND ON TO
THE HOME OF THE DRUM IN THE VALLEY.

AND THEN THERE WAS NOTHING BUT THE
LONELY SOUND OF THE TRUMPET IN THE HILLS,
AS THE FIRST STARS CAME OUT IN THE
DARKENING SKY. WHEN THAT CEASED,
THE TRUMPET HAD GONE INTO THE HOUSE
AND CLOSED THE DOOR.

THE TRUMPET HAD COME HOME TO
HIS DISTANT FARM ON THE DISTANT HILL.